PSYCHIATRY AND PSYCHOLOGY

PSYCHIATRY AND PSYCHOLOGY

Relationships, Intra-Relationships, and Inter-Relationships

By

HIRSCH LAZAAR SILVERMAN, Ph.D., D.Sc.

Professor of Psychology
Graduate School of Education
Yeshiva University
New York City

Foreword by

HAROLD MICHAL-SMITH, Ph.D.

Associate Professor of Clinical Psychiatry
New York Medical College
Chief of Psychology
Department of Pediatrics
Flower and Fifth Avenue Hospitals
Metropolitan Medical Center
New York City

Introduction by

MORTON M. STERN, M.D., F.A.P.A.

Chief, Psychiatric Department
Martland Medical Center
Newark, New Jersey

CHARLES C THOMAS • PUBLISHER
Springfield • Illinois • U.S.A.

Published and Distributed Throughout the World by

CHARLES C THOMAS • PUBLISHER

BANNERSTONE HOUSE

301-327 East Lawrence Avenue, Springfield, Illinois, U.S.A.

With THOMAS BOOKS careful attention is given to all details of manufacturing and design. It is the Publisher's desire to present books that are satisfactory as to their physical qualities and artistic possibilities and appropriate for their particular use. THOMAS BOOKS will be true to those laws of quality that assure a good name and good will.

Printed in the United States of America

FOREWORD

IN this comprehensive evaluation of the fields of psychiatry and psychology, Dr. Hirsch Lazaar Silverman interprets the individual disciplines not as singularly different and differing fields, but as related sciences with mental health purposes that are collateral, articulative, contiguous, integrative and ancillary.

Professor Silverman defines the subject sciences evaluatively: *Psychiatry* as a branch of medicine concerned with the study, treatment, and prevention of emotional, social, and spiritual maladjustments, with the goal to achieve greater individual and social maturity, to enhance human satisfactions and happiness, and to encourage constructive living; and *Psychology* as a bio-social science using experimental, observational, psychometric, clinical, and statistical methods, with directed concern for investigation of man's behavior in his encompassing environment.

This study deals logically and systematically with the relationships between psychology and psychiatry as allied sciences, the clinical aspects of both disciplines, the relationships between psychiatrists and psychologists, the implementation of psychotherapy, and recommendations for ways of interaction and improved relations. The thesis is maintained that both disciplines must come to a still better understanding professionally, based on collaboration, cooperation and association. Dr. Silverman here again makes an outstanding and sound argument for scientific methodology, professionalism, and moral integrity for both fields.

Summarily, the need for more collaborative research in

both psychiatry and psychology, with emphasis in the special areas of diagnosis and therapy, in this study is provocatively stressed; and throughout, Dr. Silverman expounds the view that individuals are biological, social, cultural, and inter-personal entities.

I compliment Dr. Silverman on his scholarly and sound evaluation and interpretation of the fields of psychology and psychiatry. In addition to his full-time position as Professor of Psychology in the Graduate School of Education of Yeshiva University, Dr. Silverman serves with distinction as Research Consulting Psychologist in the M/R Clinic of the New York Medical College. As my colleague and friend for whom I have always had greatest respect and admiration, and with particular regard for his noteworthy contributions in the academic, clinical and community settings, I write the Foreword to *PSYCHIATRY AND PSYCHOLOGY: Relationships, Intra-Relationships, and Inter-Relationships* with sincere pleasure; and recommend this study for its incisive scholarship and erudition.

HAROLD MICHAL-SMITH, PH.D.

INTRODUCTION

In the following essay Dr. Silverman presents very well the manifold relationships between psychiatry and psychology. We see from the discussion how harmonious and cross-fertilizing is the dialogue between the two, save in the area of psychotherapy. Here the tensions exist not so much between the half-sister disciplines but rather between psychiatrists and psychologists, particularly clinical psychologists. The symbol of this conflict is the M.D. degree as the basic prerequisite for the practice of psychotherapy. Obviously one's view in the matter is largely determined by his professional identification and concomitant emotional investment. So great has the latter determinant become that in this area the dialogue has taken on the overtones of ideological and religious dialectic with claims of primary and exclusive possession of the truth.

Ideally one would wish for the type of cooperation that Dr. Silverman proposes and perhaps such a pattern will evolve. But for the present and forseeable future we must face the situation as it really is: the only official communication possible between the two disciplines in this area and at this time is that of dialectic with each side watchful of its own interests. Any concession by psychiatrists will eventually lead to detachment of mental healing from the main body of medicine. Any concession by psychologists will deflect them from their goal of establishing themselves as full fledged psychotherapists. Under the shadow of these possibilities there can be only a day to day modus operandi involving local, informal and individual exchanges but not full-hearted collaboration.

Well, then, is this a deplorable situation? No, not at all. Psychiatry is firmly established as the guarantor of prime service to the mentally and emotionally ill because of its major contribution in past and present. With its intrinsic connection to psychodynamics and physiodynamics its potential for further service on a high level is greatly increased. Against this guarantee the independent or competitive contributions of clinical psychology or any other discipline pursuing its goal from another direction than that of psychiatry can only add to the public welfare. And if any discipline can overmatch or even match the past and present service of psychiatry then perhaps such competition should be preferred to formal collaboration.

MORTON M. STERN., M.D., F.A.P.A.

CONTENTS

PSYCHIATRY AND PSYCHOLOGY

THE topic of the relationships between psychology and psychiatry can be discussed from many aspects; it may even cover wide areas in which there is an obvious connection between these two distinct fields of study and practice. Although not many evaluations have been written on this topic from a general point of view, a few have appeared on the relationships between psychology and psychiatry in specific areas, such as in testing and diagnosis, psychotherapy, legal aspects of problems that arise from treatment of patients, the relationships between psychologists and psychiatrists, and other specific issues. The reasons for the lack of literature on this subject are many, but it is not the purpose nor the function of this study to delve into them.

Yet, it seems that this fact is quite symptomatic of the nature of the relationship between the two fields. It is a symptom indicating the absence of real accord and concord. It also indicates that psychologists and psychiatrists are using the mechanism of denial in relation to existing conflicts between the two disciplines.

In addition, there seems to be a much deeper and intrinsic cause for the absence of "talk" about the subject: psychology has branched out into many areas of investigation and it is not easy to define precisely which one or ones of these areas are most bound to contribute to psychiatry. Neither can one specify precisely how and where psychiatry does function, or what are its limits and substance. This lack of clearly defined areas necessarily creates confusion and misunderstanding between the two, and thus the reluctance

3

of many people in the field to commit themselves to any particular theory or even possible solutions to issues.

For many years the fields of psychiatry and psychology have been looked upon as different entities. Even today, with great scientific achievements giving hope for advancements never before known in the field of human relations, these two very closely knit professions keep themselves apart through basic misunderstandings. (To be sure, personal bias and mistrust have unfortunately done much to foster these misunderstandings.) On the other hand, there have been professional approaches, such as the psychiatric team approach, which have done much to alter this backward thinking, helping these two professions to work hand in hand towards the raising of mental health standards. It is basically for the purpose of better standards of health for all individuals that the men and women of the two professions should push forward their efforts in the first place. Rather than re-emphasize and reiterate the diverging opinions of the two professions, the field of science should try to consolidate thinking towards ways in which the ultimate goal of working as allied professions may be accomplished, with the goal of raising mental health conditions in our society and the helping of those who are mentally ill.

Both professions are caught in the dilemma of having too little knowledge for the amount of responsibility assumed by those in both professions. While not decreasing the amount of responsibility assumed, both professions should realize their common ground and then work towards the common goal. Diverging opinions between the two professions should be used for constructive purposes rather than immature bickering. We all realize that mistakes are not limited to psychiatry or psychology alone, that mistakes and misconceptions are inherent in both as they are in all professions.

For an examiner looking at the psychologist-psychiatrist relationship objectively, it is very difficult to describe a clear-cut state of affairs. Past events in the growth of science as a whole may give us a clue as to the attitudes that psychologists and psychiatrists need to incorporate into their thinking with reference to each other. We know that great advances in science, or in any field of study, have been the outgrowth of the combined knowledge of many minds, and in the long run it makes little difference in the results whether the title of the persons involved was biologist, chemist, philosopher, psychiatrist or psychologist.

However, in practical day-to-day affairs, we find it convenient, perhaps even necessary, to make these distinctions. We like to know precisely into what niche we fit, for many reasons—economic considerations, questions of status in our society, personal satisfactions in having achieved a particular goal in our lives. But these smaller considerations need not interfere with the *large* issues that face psychologists and psychiatrists in the quest for knowledge and insight into the problems of human beings. It makes little or no difference to the person under treatment what the category of the benefactor is, as long as he is adequately qualified through professional training and personal capabilities.

Since the relationship between psychiatry and psychology is a dynamic and symbiotic one, it would appear proper and necessary to conceive this relationship to be an inter-relationship, one in which the flow of influence is reciprocal. It is fundamental to an understanding of the inter-relationship between two disciplines that a definition and delineation of each be made.

Since the birth of the American Psychiatric Association in 1844, psychology has come a long way on the road of progress toward a better world of understanding between its close "rival" in the field of better health, psychiatry. Since Benjamin Rush wrote *Diseases of the Mind* (1830) and James Prichards wrote *A Treatise on Insanity* (1835), psychology has had considerable growth. Where Rush consulted the writings of psychologists for the light they might throw on the disorder of the mind, psychiatry has now begun to use the mass of experimental and empirical research for aid in its work. Where Prichards disregarded psychology and philosophy and concerned himself with a description of the disorders of the mind, there are now more and more references in the books of psychiatry to psychology. Psychiatry is gradually finding out new vistas are opening up for psychology and giving them *terra incognite* in its related professional science.

In this research, we shall attempt to combine the inductive method with the deductive in the following way: we shall discuss general issues in psychiatry and psychology; and then, whenever the content permits, intersperse examples of concrete nature, or of empirical validity. In such a way we hope to give a picture of the essential relationships between psychology and psychiatry. This evaluation will cover, as much as possible, topics which seem of general importance and which logically divide the subject matter in a natural way, including the relationship between psychology (as science) and psychiatry; the relationship between clinical psychology and clinical psychiatry; the relationship between psychologists and psychiatrists; the status of psychotherapy in its relation to psychology and psychiatry; and recommendations for ways of interaction and improved relations.

Before going on to the body of this study, one more point should be made to clarify a stand upon which not all psychologists might agree. It is assumed in this evaluation that the goal and function of both psychology and psychiatry are the promotion of mental health among people. Certain experimentally-minded psychologists may claim that their interest is solely within scientific limits and that experimental psychology has little to do with human beings. It is the conviction of the writer that such claims might well express the opinions of their claimants but they do not reflect the true motives of these psychologists. They, too, are working for the welfare of people; but simply claim to be "more orthodox than the Pope" in their scientific quest.

I

WHILE one may safely state that the fields of psychiatry and psychology as "theoretical" sciences are as old as history, in its scope and contemporary methods psychology is relatively a newcomer to the family of the "pure" sciences. Of course, we now refer to experimental psychology which can claim that it is following scientific principles and its methodology is that of science. But experimental psychology today is mainly concerned with animal behavior and most authorities in psychology still find it improper to generalize from such findings to human behavior. Yet, it is well known that the implications of the work of the experimentalists is taken up by others as scientific principles. The results brought from Pavlov's animal laboratories are looked upon as pertaining to humans as much as to animals. American psychologists continued the Pavlovian line to such an extent as to apply the methods of conditioning to hospital patients. Skinner, for example, has succeeded in having psychotic patients respond to the environment as they have never before done. He used conditioning techniques to achieve such results. This is only one example of how psychology as a science is applied to psychiatric problems and the way in which cooperation between the two disciplines can work effectively.[20]

Another way in which psychology can be used in psychiatric problems is of course the discovery by experimental psychologists of standards of behavior upon which the psychiatrist can base his judgments of normality or abnormality. This is particularly obvious in the field of drugs, or what is now called "psychopharmacology." The psychologists in the laboratory search for methods and procedures which best make for recording behavior that is characteristic of certain species in certain conditions. Then the psychiatrist performs whatever new conditions and factors he wants to experiment with; for example, he might introduce drugs or perform an operation. The psychologist in turn compares the changes in the behavior of the organism before and after administration of the drug and provides, if at all, some interpretation for the results from a psychological point of view. The psychiatrist is then able to evaluate such results both in the light of psychological explanations and from a chemical or neurological aspect.

But from a general point of view psychology provides psychiatry with a theory of human behavior which is not altogether based on a specific case history nor on an indefinite number of details. A theory of human behavior is an abstraction and its value is its applicability to every case, or its universality. Only a psychological theory which encompasses the human being as a whole can hope to survive; and, therefore, the holistic approach is the order of the day. But such an approach could not have been achieved by psychologists were it not for those who know something about the physiological functioning of the organism. After all, psychological problems arise many times because of some organic malfunctioning. Thus, one may surmise that while scientific psychology provides for a framework of principles and dynamics which might explain behavior and its deviations, psychiatry throws light on the organic and physiological aspects and ties these aspects in their relation to manifestations of behavior.

In order to discuss further the relationship of psychology to psychiatry, let us first define basic terms. The New York State Advisory Council in Psychology has adopted the following definition of psychological practice:[47] "A person practices psychology within the meaning of this Act (Article 153 of the New York State Education Law, 1956) when he renders to individuals, organizations or the public, any service involving the application of principles, methods or procedures of understanding, predicting or influencing behavior, such as the principles pertaining to learning, perception, motivation, thinking, emotions, or interpersonal relationships; or of constructing, administering, or interpreting tests of mental abilities, aptitudes, interests, attitudes, personality characteristics, emotions, or motivation; or of assessing public opinion. The application of said principles and methods includes, but is not restricted to, diagnosis, prevention, and amelioration of emotional disorders and adjustment problems of individuals and groups; educational and vocational planning; personnel selection and management; the arrangement of effective work and learning situations; advertising and market research; the resolution of interpersonal and social conflicts, lecturing on or teaching of psychology; and the design and conduct of applied psychological research."

Menninger[19] defines psychiatrist as "a doctor of the mind rather than of the brain. This means that he is concerned with the physical and chemical phases of life, to be sure, but more especially the psychological and social. He studies behavior abnormalities in the large, not merely reflexes and sensation changes." Elsewhere he states that "psychiatry is an organized science, art, and profession linked in a three-way combination with medicine, psychology, and sociology. It is a branch of medicine, a branch in which the psychological factors in human characterology are given more recognition and consideration both in diagnosis and in treatment than is the case in the routine practice of the internist, obstetrician, or surgeon. Such psychological emphasis, however, cannot ignore the psychology of the rest of the human environment, since no patient lives in a vacuum or on a desert island. In this way psychiatry is, very naturally, and properly, bringing sociologists, psychologists and physicians closer together and from this there would appear to be evolving at the present time a new concept of human beings. The essence of this new concept in its broadest sense is that human beings possess a physical and chemical and psychological structure partly self-determined, partly socially determined. This is most apparent in the psychological factor but it, in turn, modifies the physical and chemical reactions of each individual."

From these definitions it can be quite easily seen, even before further details are considered, that the two disciplines are related in many ways. However, in addition to being related it is significant to indicate statistically the impact of psychological work on psychiatry. The *American Journal of Psychiatry* published a report in 1956[25] covering the period from January 1944 through December 1955 which reviewed the contributions of psychologists to the field of psychiatry. The authors found that " (1) Articles authored by psychologists ranged from 1.5 percent in 1944 to 5.4 percent in 1951. Forty-one, or about 3 percent of the total articles (1,319 were reviewed) were authored by psychologists. (2) Articles in which psychologists were listed as co-authors ranged from 4.6 percent in 1944 to 10 percent in 1947. Ninety-seven or approximately 7 percent were co-authored by psychologists. (3) All in all, psychologists had a hand in 138 or 10 percent of the 1,319 contributions published in the *American Journal of Psychiatry* during the eleven year period studied."

Referring again to the definition of psychological practice as accepted by New York State in its certification law, we find many areas where psychology and psychiatry are closely related. Proper methodology is one of psychology's greatest contributions to psychiatry. Not only in applied psychiatry but in research, it is obvious that no interdisciplinary research can be better than the behavioral measures which provide its dependent variable or variables. Yet the fact remains that the behavioral methods used in interdisciplinary research are commonly inferior to the behavioral methods available at the time, and there are many examples of the use of research techniques outmoded by two or more decades. This is probably just as true of the anatomical, physiological, and biochemical methods used by the behavioral scientists. However, the best safeguard against correlating results obtained from outmoded techniques lies in the formation of research teams representing members of both or all the disciplines whose data are related. Here again is where the services of the psychologist can be invaluable to the work of the psychiatrist.

To be sure, the functions of the psychiatrist are somewhat more clearly defined than those of the psychologist. The area in which the psychiatric team performs is, in most instances, a hospital; and in such an institution, the psychiatrist assumes the leadership in giving direction to the program and in integrating the "team" and its functioning. He formulates the over-all strategy, and approaches each patient with a dynamic and generally developmental point of view.

The relationships of psychiatry and psychology are still more poignant. In becoming a science of human behavior, psychology found that many thousands of individuals who felt emotionally conflicted and unhappy started to come to psychologists for help; and one of its main branches, Clinical Psychology, arose to supply the needs of these individuals, to help in diagnosing and treating their mental disturbances. Before there was a science of human behavior, people went to their physician for help when they experienced emotional disturbance; medicine, therefore, had to develop a psychiatric arm for the diagnosis and treatment of psychological problems and ailments.

Psychiatry has been gaining in prestige and status. As Menninger[43] notes: "Psychiatry has arrived . . . a lowly and obscure medical discipline, practiced by a few . . . rising to heights of considerable importance through sheer force of clinical necessity." Psychoanalysis was the major influence on psychiatry in the first half of this century.[29] Today it is difficult to isolate psychoanalytic contributions from the total context of psychiatry, because there has been an integration of psychoanalytic theory with the biological and social sciences. The special fields in psychiatry are: Shock therapy, psychosurgery, pharmacological therapy, individual therapy, conditioned reflex therapy, and group therapy. American psychiatry is a psycho-sociobio-medico-psychoanalytic composite. The psychiatrist can be a case consultant, teacher and legal protector, as well as the doctor who treats the mentally ill.

Arieti[5] states: "Perhaps no other field of human endeavor is so encompassing and difficult to define as that of Psychiatry. Like his fellow scientists, the psychiatrist must be aware of the developments in a score of related fields. Unlike his fellow scientists however, he extends his investigations to the subjective world of the individual and must include in all of its aspects the drama of man. Thus the psychiatrist searches areas which were, until recently, reserved to the intuition of the poet and the artist and to the speculation of the philosopher."

At this point, it is best briefly to define psychiatry, its functions and roles in still more delineating terms, so as to understand the meaningful relationships between the psychiatrist and the psychologist, their differences and the necessary dependencies. Psychiatry is a medical specialty, which deals with the prevention, diagnosis, treatment and care of mental and neurotic illnesses and other problems relating to personal adjustment. Psychiatry developed from the purely medical field as an art which took care of the mentally ill. From this early art, the science of analysis and therapy arose, thereby providing an additional service, based on medical principles and practices.[16] The psychiatrist, in his work, is trained as a physician first. His training in medicine affords the psychiatrist the distinctive advantage of working not only with the human body, but on it as well.[2] Like the psychologist, the psychiatrist is interested in abnormal, deviant behavior.

Let us consider certain areas of deviancy, however briefly. Psychiatric illnesses fall into three groups: psychoses (with gross systems of distortion, hallucination, delusions, phantasy, etc., and where the personality is disrupted); psychoneuroses (lesser symptoms of hysteria, anxiety, obsessions, compulsions, but where there is much hold on the personality and reality); and psychosomatic illness (in which manifestations are primarily physical with at least a partial emotional cause). In treating these, the psychiatrist makes use of medical forms of therapy, like chemotherapy (ataractics), shock treatment (insulin and electric), use of the encephalogram, physiotherapy, recreation, occupational therapy, and others.

Psychiatry may be further defined as related to the scientific discipline of biology. It is occupied also in the study, treatment, and prevention of personal, emotional, social, and spiritual maladjustments. It is interested in making its contribution to the attainment of greater individual and social maturity and adjustment, and the enhancement of human satisfaction and happiness. The traditional definition of psychiatry, as that branch of medicine which deals with diseases of the mind, is rapidly disappearing.

The study, care and treatment of the definitely mentally sick in institutions, although important, occupies relatively the smaller part in a program which seeks to achieve the objectives and ideals of modern psychiatry,[32] even though perhaps 97 percent of those with major mental illness are treated in institutions at some time. Greater emphasis is being placed on the understanding and treatment of the vast army of so-called psychoneurotics, who remain in everyday life, but because of unsolved emotional conflicts, show various and often serious degrees of anxiety, ineffectiveness, and unhappiness; alcoholism, which entails an enormous wastage of potentially adequate and much needed mental capacity; juvenile delinquency, so often determined by deficits in parent-childhood relationships and environments in early life; mental hygiene, and particularly the mental hygiene of childhood; vocational guidance; industrial psychiatry; and treatment of many other human frailties.

It should be pointed out that in psychiatry the concept of "normal" is used to indicate the concept of average or typical behavior. This, however, does not necessarily infer that normal is the opposite of sickness or pathology. It is merely an expression of the range in which behavior falls and is considered to be not deviant. Unfortunately, the largest problem in differentiating between normal and the not normal is that this concept is basically culturally determined. What may be considered normal in western civilization, such as man assuming the aggressive rather than woman, would be considered to be abnormal in many of the societal tribes studied by anthropologists in South Africa. Within the confines of the normal, there are wide variations from a true, exact norm, for there is some narcissism, sadism, love, hate, fear, aggression, and the like in all of us. In addition to the concept that each individual possesses all types of characteristics not necessarily congruent with his personality, it must also be noted that behavior in each individual is qualitatively different, with the differences manifested in degrees and patterns of behavior. Thus, it is not difficult to see, upon careful analysis of the term "normal," that it is a difficult word to define, and for all intents and purposes, is a nebulous concept which really no longer has any bearing on present day nosology.

As Lewis indicates, "Present day psychiatry is an odd mixture of internal medicine, neurology, psychology, clinical testing, 'psychosurgery' and various drug assaults on the personality, mental hygiene, philosophical speculation and the pseudoscientific diagnosis applied by those who operate on the margins of the specialty."[36]

What, then, *does* the psychiatrist study? He studies the organism as a whole in relation to his environment, and to his society. He places each activity performed by the organism into a context to see how it relates to people, and how people relate to it. He studies the individual, his mind, and his body, in relation to his society and his culture and the adjustment he has made to it. Thus, a person's behavior may be "abnormal," but if the organism is adjusted to his behavior, and if it plays no major role in his acceptance by people, then abnormal as it is, the behavior does not warrant study; for the organism is "adjusted." Thus, the basic problem faced by the psychiatrist is getting his patients to adjust to the society with whatever problems of limitations they may have. In order to determine the degree of adjustment or maladjustment, the psychiatrist works hand in hand with the psychologist, and a social worker. To the psychiatrist, the reduction of stress, and increase in support by changes that can be made in the environment, are often as important as the maintenance of good mental health in the heretofore undisturbed patient.

Summarily, then, psychiatry is a branch of medicine concerned with the study, treatment, and prevention of emotional, social, and spiritual maladjustments. Its goal is to achieve greater individual and social maturity, to enhance human satisfactions and happiness, and to encourage constructive living. Psychiatry is "the science of human behavior, its determining factors, the techniques of its analysis, its vicissitudes and aberrations, and the methods that may be employed to align behavior with desired social norms."[39]

The specialties of the psychiatrist are psychotherapy, mental hygiene, psychoanalysis, child psychiatry,[35] and others. Psychiatry's objectives at the present time are to find the relationship between the chemistry of the central nervous system and behavior through research, to increase the understanding of the human personality and behavior in sickness and in health, as well as to treat mental disorders.

But psychology is also a science. It is a bio-social science, using experimental, observational, quantitative, clinical, and statistical methods. It is also the scientific investigation of behavior—of man in his social and material environment. Psychology is also the utilization of such science as it is applied in professional ways. The application of the facts and findings of "pure" psychological science is being made today in dozens of areas. The American Psychological Association lists over twenty of these areas, including evaluation and measurement; psychological study of social issues; clinical psychology; consulting psychology; industrial and business psychology; educational psychology; school psychology; counseling and guidance; military psychology; maturity and old age; and teaching of psychology.

II

In order to understand the healthy positive relationship between psychiatry and psychology, one must first understand some of the differences between the two fields. It is basically through these differences that a fruitful relationship can be obtained. Differences between psychiatry and psychology allow for a compatibility within the psychiatric setting which is a necessity for helpful patient-centered type thinking. Although the latter statement seems paradoxical, it is at the same time a truism. For diverging opinions provoke thought which ultimately reflects new ideas and consequently the making of progress.

Basic in the history of psychiatry is the fact that there has been a very close tie between psychiatry and psychology.[7] Abnormal psychology textbooks draw heavily upon the concepts and theories of such medical men as Charcot, Janet, Prince, and, of course, Freud,[29] whose influence in many fields of psychology is extensive, aside from the direct and recognized impact of his theories upon clinical psychology.

It is, perhaps, the emergence into prominence in modern thought of the concepts of the Whole, the *Gestalt*, the interacting unity of mind and body, of Psyche and Soma, that has tended most strongly to bring together psychiatry and psychology. The vast literature growing up in present medical and psychological studies in which the "total" person is the subject for study further underlines the close relationship between psychiatry and psychology.[15]

There has been a two directional exchange between psychology and psychiatry, resulting in a close association of

17

interest and function between the two professions, although their respective backgrounds differ. Both groups have their primary and final interest centered in the welfare of people. Both psychology and psychiatry branched off from different scientific disciplines: behavioral science and medicine. Both are almost accidental contenders for the goal of helping individuals with emotional problems, since neither was specifically designed to be all inclusive or all-knowing in relation to these emotional problems, but each becomes available to attempt some solutions when faced with dire human needs.

Psychology has been defined as the science of the psyche, or the mind; and psychiatry is defined on the same level as the medical science of mental disorder (including diagnosis and treatment). While psychology in general is related to psychiatry, it is perhaps clinical psychology which has the most intimate symbiotic inter-relationship with it. The difficulty of accurately defining this term is compounded by the several bases, for such a definition could be made according to content, method, purpose, or practice, which will be dealt with subsequently in this evaluation.

The psychiatrist's orientation is medical. He has training in medicine, in pharmacology, and in neurology. The psychologist's training, while it involves also a study of the nervous system, includes as part of its training certain tools, projective and psychological tests, which aid the psychologist in formulating the kind of treatment a given patient may require. These instruments, though not infallible, used with clinical experience can enable the psychologist to know the resources the individual has, and can aid in deciding what kind of treatment from which he can best profit, and to see if he can profit from treatment at all.

Menninger credits psychology for bringing to psychiatry and medicine a tradition of objective measurement, of clearly defined logic, of proper methodological procedure which clinical practice and clinical thinking may tend to cause medical people to forget. "Traditional psychiatric nosology has finally been forced into open bankruptcy largely by the penetrating symptomatological analyses made by the psychologists. And a very healthy state of affairs it is, I say. We can now begin to define with a precision long absent from our work the clinical factors—psychological and otherwise—which characterize similar syndromes. . . . This has led to our irrevocable affiliation . . . whether, in the course of events, the therapeutic function of the psychologist will develop and find its proper place in the same way that the therapeutic function of the X-rays has found its place, we can only guess. I should expect it to do so. . . . Psychiatrists should not be surprised that psychologists are not yet fully accustomed to their new clinical role. Psychologists similarly should not be surprised if the medical profession, jealous of its historical and traditional responsibilities, is somewhat slow in welcoming the psychologists. In my own mind there is no doubt that the time will come when the assistance of the psychologists in the diagnosis, let us say of cancer or arthritis, will be taken as a matter of everyday routine by the internist, and when the treatment of certain types of illnesses by the psychologist associated with the psychiatrist will be taken as standard procedure."[19]

Psychology, then, is a science of human behavior. It is the science of the entire individual in all his aspects: a psychologist being one with knowledge of the methods and facts of the science.[14]

Psychiatry has been defined as a branch of medicine which treats mental illness; on the other hand, psychology is the science which studies the functions of the mind, such as sensation, perception, memory, thought, and, more broadly, the behavior of an organism in relation to its environment.[41] These two definitions present a clearcut but certainly not a very stimulating picture of these two disciplines; and a more interpretive evaluation appears warranted.

The sphere of psychology encompasses the study of the

mentally ill, the neurotic, and the retarded. Until such abnormalities of behavior came within its scope, psychology was concerned in former years primarily with investigation of processes, vision, perception, learning, etc., which are relativisms in all human beings. Emphasis was on the process itself, not on individual manifestations of it. Interest in individual difference finally developed. When psychologists were finally led to undertake further investigations, they developed the concept of personality, a concept which takes into consideration not only psychological process but also the combined characteristic pattern which all of these exhibit in particular individuals.[37] Medicine (and particularly that branch of it known as psychiatry) played a leading part in the broadening of psychological interests.

Thus we see that the whole person is now being considered and as such there is the blending of psychiatry and psychology with the wholesome benefits accruing to the individual. Man functions holistically as a complete organism, with the psyche (mind) and soma (body) acting together. The only difference between "somatic" and mental illness is that the symptoms in one case are heavier on the somatic side, and in the other on the emotional side. An illness is never wholly one or the other. Every somatic occurrence in health or sickness is in the emotional depths of the individual, and all emotional states are manifested in the body.

Even the use of opinion polls and market research are important psychological factors to psychiatry. Social psychologists such as Redlich and Hollingshead[52] point out how social class and economic status affect one's treatment as a patient, one's diagnosis and theoretical attitude. The prevalence of a particular attitude toward psychiatry in general and certain techniques in particular, such as psychoanalysis and tranquillizers, on the part of the public as ascertained through market research surveys and opinion polls, to some extent has an impact on psychiatry as a profession. Legislation desired by psychiatrists is aided by knowing the public's attitudes, desires, and needs.

Motivational research as carried on by psychologists, such as Ernest Dichter, in addition to uncovering information as to consumers' wants and desires is also helpful in uncovering what is "wrong" with people. When far more money is spent on escapism than on education and mental health, an understanding of the mechanisms involved is essential. Certainly there is nothing wrong with people enjoying their lives to the utmost; but when enjoyment is purely an escape and life's more important factors are rejected, it seems imperative to understand the motivations of the public through use of psychological methods to correct the situation.

To a scientist in the field of mental health, it is evident that psychiatry and psychology interact most in this area.[50] It is in places where work is done with ill people (and not merely in laboratories), where theory is applied to everyday problems, that psychologists and psychiatrists enjoy a meeting-of-the-mind and discuss their mutual patients. But before discussing what these relations are, or might be, let us examine what is meant by "clinical psychology." Clinical psychology may be defined in three frames of reference.[6, 28, 42] One is associated with certain names of persons closely identified with the field. In this category are included such names as Binet, Witmer, Terman, Wells, Gesell, Goodenough, Healy. The second frame of reference includes "those disciplines outside of psychology proper that have looked to psychological science for aid in solution of their special problems and so have served as stimuli to the clinical psychologists in extending their fields . . . These are community interests, such as schools, courts, and prisons." The third frame of reference appertains "to personality conceived of as in more than one dimension." By so defining clinical psychology, Beck implicitly is retelling the history of the development of clinical psychology which is the offspring of both the medical and the sociological disciplines. Such a definition also implies the general trend in today's behavioral sciences of trying to look at the individual as one piece and treating him as such. Consequently, such a philosophy of the human being had to have its effects on the way psychologists treated their subject matter.

It is certainly established that every individual desiring or needing psychological or psychiatric help should have a thorough physical examination before any diagnosis or treatment of mental disorder is attempted; this is common knowledge to both psychiatrist and psychologist alike. (It has been estimated that between 70 and 80 per cent of those so examined have been reported negative by physicians. Obviously, the psychologist or psychiatrist cannot handle any of the other 20 or 30 per cent alone.) If we discount the cases where organic basis for mental disturbance exists and a physician then gives treatment, what are the positions of psychiatrist and psychologist with reference to the other cases? Perhaps by classifying these cases a relationship may become apparent. These large categories are as follows,[9] in order of increasing severity: (1) Transient situational personality disorders; (2) Personality disorders (psychopathic personality); (3) psychoneurotic disorders; (4) Psychophysical autonomic and visceral disorders; (5) Psychotic disorders; (6) Mental deficiency; (7) Chronic brain disorders; and (8) Acute brain disorders.

The last two categories, those of chronic and acute brain disorders, belong assuredly in the hands of the physician or psychiatrist because of their obvious need for medication. However, the psychologist has an important role in the testing procedures that precede diagnosis, to permit the evaluation of the kind and amount of damage to the brain.

The area of mental deficiency again involves a great deal of testing, as well as complete case history and physical study. The psychologist's contribution to the complete clinical picture can be of major proportions; in this case, he is also capable of handling the therapy, both for the deficient individual and other members of his family to enable the individual to adjust to the world and to benefit fully from whatever training he is capable of taking.

In her evaluation of psychologists and psychiatrists, Luszki[38] writes: "Psychologists and psychiatrists are persons with many similar characteristics. A study indicates that persons receiving graduate training in clinical psychology and in psychiatry resemble one another much more closely than do those in psychiatry and general medicine. In a great many important areas psychologists and psychiatrists feel and think alike, maintain the same general orientation, and develop similar personality structures. Despite these similarities, the psychiatrist is almost always accorded higher status. He is often given this status even in research situations where the psychologist feels he knows much more than the psychiatrist, and is much better equipped. Psychiatrists and psychologists start out with different value systems in relation to research. Psychiatrists are interested in research of an exploratory character, and in discovering something new. Psychologists are interested in proof. There is a difference in pacing and in timing. The psychiatrist has his experience and his intimate acquaintance with patients as his criterion of evidence; the criterion of the psychologist is based on statistical tests."

We see now that psychology is the branch of objective science which deals with behavior, actions or mental processes, and with the organism, or part of an organism which elicits the behavioral response. Psychology began as a science dealing with empirical facts, and their functional relationships, and attempted to explain these facts from a purely philosophical point of view. To explain data, whether on clinical cases or animal experiments, scientists were forced to take philosophical positions, on mentalism, operationism and the mind-body problem. From their various metatheories, psychologists were then able to deduce schools of thought, or theories on the nature of man's behavior, why he acts the way he does, the reasons for his psychic adequacies and inadequacies. From an extensive amount of theorizing in psychology arose the applied school of clinical psychology, a branch of psychology which was not a thought or theory set aside on its own, but an extensive, comprehensive approach to the treatment and analysis of deviant psychological behavior. In its analysis of behavior disorders, clinical psychology uses the tool of the syndrome, or collection of patterned symptoms, similar to the way physicians might diagnose and differentiate an ordinary head cold from a brain tumor, with the same manifesting symptom, the headache. Just as clinical medicine uses the practice of differential diagnosis in its medical evaluation, so does psychology use this, as a diagnostic aid.

The psychologist is prepared to diagnose behavioral disorders by exhaustive study of learning, comparative psychology, developmental psychology, psychoanalytical theory, social psychology and a study of the abnormal and the normal behavioral patterns manifest in our society. The psychologist works in close association with the medical profession and is of aid in the diagnosis and treatment of mental deviation. Ofttimes, the psychologist is a member of a psychiatric team, which is prepared, each in his own area, to bring forth the fullest amount of data and relevant information possible on each patient.[44] The psychologist, from his end of the team, is prepared to offer to the medical, measurements of mental ability, both abstract and concrete, projective material and records from the many diagnostic tools available, information on attitudes, prejudices, emotionality, attention and concentration ability, and a host of other variables, all proven necessities for diagnosis in the field. This data,[62] taking the form it does, and uncovering heretofore hidden variables and characteristics, are as important to medicine and psychiatry as urine analysis and blood tests. Menninger again supports this fact, stating "The diagnostic function of the clinical psychologist is now so well established in psychiatry, that the competent psychiatrist . . . would no more exclude the special techniques of the psychologist in his diagnostic studies than would a capable physician exclude the findings of a roentgenologist."[19]

According to psychiatrists, psychology is mainly a method (projective techniques) for studying individuals. Still others regard clinical psychology, in terms of its purpose, as an ancillary profession. To those who examine its content, clinical psychology is the science of psychodynamics. In terms of the practice of clinical psychology, as a member of the psychiatric "team," the psychologist operates under the aegis of the psychiatrist in fluid and as yet undelimited ways which include, according to the specific setting in which they function, testing, diagnosis, and psychotherapy.[45] There are, to be sure, very many roles and very many functions, all dependent on the setting in which the psychologist functions. As an example, the Veterans Administration summarizes the role of clinical psychology as follows: "VA policies at present encourage the maximum utilization of the skills and knowledge of clinical psychologists. The primary need is for psychological help in diagnosis, training, research, and education. In psychodiagnosis and psychotherapy, the psychologist functions under the supervision of a psychiatrist."

A further complicating factor in the evaluation of "contribution" of the disciplines is the distinction between psychology and psychiatry. Strictly speaking, the psychologist (note agent suffix) is a practitioner who applies knowledge of the psyche to problems of mind and behavior, whereas the psychiatrist (iatros=physician) makes use of the healing arts and the science of psychology (knowledge of) in treating the mentally ill. Such close association of interest and function between two professions, with backgrounds different in as many ways as they resemble each other, inevitably provoke situations in which conflict and competition can develop, but offer an equal potential for productive collaboration.

But clinical psychology, unlike experimental or child psychology, is not a subdivision or field of general psychology; rather, it is a variety of applied psychology, and, as such, is more closely related to personal psychology and human engineering and psychotherapy. Clinical psychology, however, draws upon and utilizes the facts, principles, and techniques of all fields of psychology. The term "clinical" is borrowed from its medical usage. Originally it meant "of or pertaining to a bed," but even in current medical practice its usage is no longer limited to the individual whose problem is of such a nature as to require the clinician to visit him at his bed. Today, "clinical" applied to any specialty means only that the person is being studied and regarded as an individual, not as a member of a larger group. In one way, then, it may be said that clinical psychology is applied psychology of the individual.[51]

The application of psychology to the individual, however, is in no sense restricted to clinical psychologists. The psychiatrist utilizes psychology along with other basic sciences. Likewise, the educational or vocational guidance counselor, the minister, and the foreman, all use psychology, even though they do not call themselves psychologists. Clinical psychology emphasizes individual variations in the capacity to deal with the everyday problems of life. Closely related to psychiatry, mental hygiene, and the sociological and educational disciplines, it is largely concerned with the clinical study of all kinds of maladjustments in children and adults. Clinical psychology emphasizes individual variations in the capacity to deal with the everyday problems of life. Unlike psychiatry, the field stresses the use of quantitative methods, such as measurements, scales, and tests, in establishing the patients' behavior patterns.

Psychologists themselves differ in their feelings on the functions of the members of the profession. Some appear to emphasize diagnosis alone. Others take diagnosis and therapy as their province, either in cooperation with psychiatrists or independently.[53] In his discussion of "clinical psychology as a psychodiagnostic art," Rosenzweig[54] states that "the clinical psychologist can help his co-workers solve problems that are most coextensive with the whole field of adjustment." He also writes, ". . . there is the increasingly important area of personality dynamics in connection with which the psychiatrist may be given assistance in the better understanding of the patient as well as in the planning and conduct of psychotherapy." His viewpoint places the clinical psychologist as part of a team, in which his part is involved both in diagnosis and in evaluation of the effects of various methods of therapy.

Psychology and psychiatry are closely related in the area of psychodiagnosis, especially because clinical psychology has both psychometric and psychodynamic origins. The clinician still uses objective instruments, but relies considerably on qualitative interview procedures and on projective techniques that are not strictly standardized and require particular skill in interpretation.[55] The projective techniques embody the psychodynamic point of view more than any other available devices, and require special qualifications of training. These are the techniques that are probably of the most value to the psychiatrist as an application of experimental methodology.

In this world, where, paradoxically, the richest nation on earth breeds (perhaps unwittingly) a great deal of poverty, where there are war-torn areas, depressions, disasters, prejudicial and racial problems, the demand for psychiatric services is a growing one. To aid the psychiatrist, the psychologist provides many useful services in addition to a basic understanding of behavior on all levels.[8] The psychologist teaches the psychiatrist about learning theory not because it expresses a systematic view of man, but because learning and understanding for the most part go hand in hand; and it is the function of the psychiatrist to teach the patient to understand, and live with what he is and what he has. Therefore, learning is an essential to understanding. Similarly, many of the other psychological principles (e.g., insight, emotion, repression, aggression) are explainable and measurable, an invaluable aid to the psychiatrist.

Psychology is, for the most part, equipped to do diagnosis

with the many psychometric and projective tools available.[24] Psychiatry is basically interested in the problem of adjustment, and how to recognize the maladjusted, in addition to how to treat him, so that he may be realigned with society and reality.

Psychologists must become more involved in the work of prevention of mental illness, than in narrowing their interests to the treatment of emotional disorders.[46] Psychological services which concentrate their efforts on the establishment of sound mental health procedures at home and in the school will result in increasingly effective programs for the "exceptional" child in the public schools, in refined techniques of learning and motivation for all children, in the early diagnosis and treatment of the emotionally disturbed child, and in the decrease in the numbers of the emotionally disturbed and socially maladjusted children in the community.

Since the school psychologist usually services a large number of children, it becomes necessary to see a small percentage of all the children who are emotionally disturbed.[48] It is in this area that the school psychologist, as a clinician, gives a full psychological examination, including projective techniques, and makes a formal diagnosis. This information, at times, can only be discovered in a careful interpretation of the projective material. The school psychologist also has a wealth of material in the actual behavior of the child which is noted by his teachers.[12] Since the psychological services in schools have been established, there has been a decrease in the age of those children referred to community treatment agencies. Children who have problems are now identified at an earlier age, and are being treated along with their parents, before their problems can become more serious.[49] Therefore, there are important implications for preventive psychological services.

As a member of an interdisciplinary team the psychologist may well participate in diagnosis, therapy and research. The psychiatrist, also, has these duties to be sure, but the difference amounts to something like this: It seems reasonable to assume that all important decisions regarding a patient should be based on neurological, physiological and other findings of the psychiatrist, on intellectual, personality and other findings of the psychologist, and on family background, cultural, and other findings of the social worker. With all findings reviewed and integrated by the team in an effort to arrive at the best decisions and recommendations, they are looking out, in the best way possible, for the patient's future welfare.

The investigation of human behavior by psychologists is approached, then, by three different methods:[4] (a) the experimental, (b) the differential or statistical, and (c) the clinical. The experimental approach involves the setting up of a hypothesis concerning some aspect of human behavior and using the time-honored scientific method of experimentation. The statistical approach again involves a hypothesis to be tested, and this is done by statistical evaluation of samples of behavior in a great many cases. The clinical approach differs from the other two in that it lacks the objective rigidity of either, but it provides information which is impossible to secure by the other methods. The American Psychological Association recommends that the term clinical psychology be used to denote "that art and technology which deals with the adjustment problems of human beings." There is agreement among authorities that clinical psychology concerns itself with both the diagnosis and treatment of the psychological problems of human beings.[17] The range of activities of the clinician varies from simple psychometrics to independent consulting where difficult problems of diagnosis and treatment are handled.[18]

It is evident from these considerations that the relationship of psychiatry to psychology depends on the branch or method of approach of the psychologist. The experimental and statistical approaches belong almost exclusively to the realm of research. The conclusions drawn from experiments and statistical evaluations are then applied by the psychiatrist and clinician in diagnosis and treatment of an individual problem. Although some important areas of human behavior cannot as yet be investigated experimentally or statistically, the contributions already made have been significant. The great body of knowledge concerning the human mind provided by psychologists is needed and used by the psychiatrist in conjunction with his own body of psychological and medical knowledge to diagnose and treat mental illness.

The clinical psychologist and the psychiatrist have a good deal in common. They both deal with the individual with a problem in an attempt to diagnose, or classify, the disorder, and to effect a worthwhile method of treatment. In what ways do they differ, and to what extent? The obvious difference is that, in this country at least, a psychiatrist is a physician. This is a most important consideration. In this day and age, it should be no longer necessary to present arguments in defense of the holistic approach to diagnosis or treatment of human illness, whether the symptoms be mental or physical. Although the psychologist studies physiology and the relationships of the various parts of the body to each other, he cannot be expected to have the quantity or quality of information which the physician acquires in the course of his specialized studies. The increasing importance of chemotherapy in both the study and treatment of mental illness further limits the functioning of the psychologist in dealing with certain types of patients.

As often happens in two closely related professions, the members in one view the members of the other as interfering; and *their* work is constantly brought into sharp criticism. This kind of relationships develops especially when there seems to be a great overlap, and, thus, misunderstanding and resentment grow. Some psychiatrists look upon some psychologists as medically ignorant, without enough knowledge and skill to deal with other human beings. On the other hand, some psychologists view some psychiatrists as having only the advantageous orientation for treating the mind because of their medical-organic background. Certainly, if one is objective enough to look at both professions honestly, one would soon come to the conclusion both viewpoints have their accuracy partly; but that a sweeping generalization cannot and should not be made. The unfortunate condition is that both professions sometimes do make generalizations on the basis of personal experience without bringing into account the total picture. However, as psychologists work more and more with psychiatrists, they get to know more and more about their colleagues and try to let these colleagues know more about themselves. In such manner, there is more and more interaction, and more coordination, for the welfare of the patient. There is more recognition these days, more than ever before, that both fields still know very little about the human mind, and without personal interest and interaction, not much may be additionally learned.

III

PSYCHOSOMATIC illness brings together the two professions of psychiatry and psychology, often at the very bedside of the patient, for each recognizes the special skills and viewpoints of the other. The psychiatrist often requests a report from the psychologist which will help to answer important questions concerning the personality, dynamics, strength, and weaknesses of the patient.

The psychologist brings to bear on these questions his special tools and techniques. These include his *tests*. We can distinguish broadly two types of tests used by the psychologist, namely, psychometric and projective.

Psychometric tests are basically the so-called tests of intelligence, aptitude, achievements, interests, etc. These have been developed and used on children, in the main, but are now sufficiently so well standardized that they can be successfully administered to any living human being, from an infant to an octogenarian, even to individuals unable to speak, see, or hear. From the administration and interpretation of, say, an intelligence test, the psychologist can ascertain considerable knowledge of, and insight into, the level of function of the testee as well as his intellectual potential.

Tracing the history of psychiatric technique, Kanner points out that ". . . biographic exploration became an obligatory part of psychiatric history taking," and that "... around the turn of the century, psychiatric interest was for the first time directed toward childhood."[30] Continuing, Kanner deals with personality in terms of psychology, and indicates that "there are four types of highly important and complement-

32

ary studies of early personality development," referring to (1) observation, (2) experimentation, (3) correlation of data, and (4) interpretation.[31] The psychological evaluation is, in part, a study of the intellectual ability of the patient which includes his weaknesses and strengths in learning, language, comprehension, and other factors. The various parts of the study are integrated and are organized into a report showing *how* the individual learns, *how much* he can learn, *how* he behaves in certain situations, and *why* he behaves as he does.

The second broad category of psychological tests is known as the projective techniques. Outstanding here are the Rorschach and the Thematic Apperception Test, but also worthy of mention are human figure drawings, the Szondi test, and the Bender Gestalt test. These, also, the psychiatrist has come to depend on evaluatively.

The Rorschach test (or method) was devised originally to have been a test of imagination. However, it became a method of studying the whole personality. From an uncertain instrument, it has became a sharp diagnostic tool. It is based on the assumption that any performance of the individual is an expression of the whole individual, and the more the performance is unstructured, the more expressive will the performance be. The responses given by the subject to the ten ink-blots which constitute the test are carefully analyzed as to what is seen, where it is seen, how it is seen, and then ratios of the various types of response categories are calculated. From this is developed and synthesized a picture of the underlying personality structure.

The personality structure can be viewed as having three main parts.[12, 37] The first is the basic personality configuration. Here we find two types of balances: the balance between spontaneity and control; and that between introversive and extroversive tendencies. The second part of the personality structure deals with intellectual aspects (the amount and kind of intelligence displayed; also the preference for inductive, deductive, or intuitive thinking; the relation between imaginative and rational functions, etc.). The third part of the personality structure has to do with the emotional aspects of personality, the emotional ties with inner life and outer reality.

The relations among the determinants indicate, for both the psychiatrist and the psychologist, the basic configuration of the personality. The balance between "form" on the one hand, and "color," "shading," and "movement" on the other, establishes the relation between control and spontaneity. The relative balance between inner promptings and other stimulation is calculated from the proportion of movement and color. (To be sure, the validity of the Rorschach technique has been established mainly by using clinical diagnosis and clinical observations as the criteria.)

At this point mention may well be made of the many contributions of projective techniques to the psychological diagnosis of organic brain damage. Zygmundt A. Piotrowski, Ph.D., was among the pioneers in the investigation of the use of the Rorschach method for the determination of "organic signs" in the protocols of the brain-damaged patient; and he found ten signs of abnormalities in the Rorschach records of a group of patients which included those with sub-cortical brain damage. Lauretta Bender, M.D., author of the Bender Gestalt test, has found that disturbances in the visual motor gestalt function as demonstrated by the copying of geometric test forms, most likely are related to lesions in the area between the temporal, parietal, and occipital lobes of the dominant hemisphere.

Psychological tests are particularly helpful to the psychiatrist in providing insights concerning the role of unconscious mental factors in the clinical picture.[55] The case load of patients is usually so heavy that the practical considerations of time preclude the expense of leisurely examining each patient with techniques such as psychoanalysis; and requires the assistance of the psychologist, who with his battery of tests, can provide valuable diagnostic assistance to the psychiatrist, and also yield important information as to the patient's intellectual capacity, the suitability of a patient for treatment and even the prognosis.

Let us recapitulate at this point, briefly at least, to reconsider certain definitions of the related disciplines. Hinsie and Shatzky define psychiatry as "the science of curing or healing disorders of the psyche,"[21] and the psyche is "the mind . . . in its own way, an 'organ' of the individual . . ." and ". . . like other organs, possesses its own form and function, its embryology, gross and microscopic anatomy, physiology and pathology."[22] To them, psychology is "the science which deals with the mind and mental processes—consciousness, sensation, ideation, memory, etc."[23]

Psychology is "the branch of science which treats of mental activities,"[26] according to Hutchings; and psychiatry is "liberally, 'mind-healing;' the body of knowledge pertaining to disorders of the mental systems."[27] Masserman regards psychiatry in these words: "Psychiatry can be broadly defined as the science of human behavior—its determining factors, the techniques of its analysis, its vicissitudes and aberrations, and the methods that may be employed to align behavior with desired social norms"[39]; and, to him, "Psychology is, literally, the 'study of mind,' and therefore a term of many meanings."[40]

But psychology is mostly associated with psychological testing. Without going through the history of psychological tests, mention should nevertheless be made of the following facts: The first clinical psychologists were in effect psychometricians, and after having had much experience with their tests, clinical interpretations were superimposed on psychometric test results. The emphasis in the beginning, and even in many circles now, was on statistics. To be sure, without such a scientific approach, psychology could not have reached today's dimensions and depth. However, we would do well to remember that, whenever we are faced with an interpretation of some test data, we must keep in mind the scientific basis of our instruments and the way they were generated.

Psychological tests are used for many purposes and in many situations. Mainly in institutional setups, these instruments are used for diagnosis and personality descriptions. The intelligence tests tell us something about the intellectual functioning of the individual and sometimes about his hidden potentialities. Thus, for example, they might indicate certain discrepancies which cannot be detected otherwise, and which tell us in what areas the individual does have more problems than in others, where he is best, what type of thinking he uses, and other matters. These tests further help us to diagnose mental defectiveness; and to determine in what kind of environment, such as educational, individuals should be placed. Perhaps the most useful test in the field of clinical psychology with relation to psychiatry is the intelligence test.

Certainly it is not the purpose of this study to carry on polemics about which test for psychiatry is most useful and which is least useful. Although intelligence tests still prove to be the most reliable of all psychological tests, their importance does not overmatch the other tests given in clinical practice. At times one test may be more important than another; and clinical experience both of psychologists and psychiatrists has proven that the importance of a test can be valued only in relation to the problem presented, and how much or how little the given test is apt to contribute to the understanding of such problem. As a case in point, the problem may be mentioned of differential diagnosis of schizophrenia and brain damage or some organic defect. While the Block Design subtest on the Wechsler has proved an invaluable tool in diagnosing brain disturbance, this subtest itself is not very valid and gives no indication of such syndrome. Therefore, other tests are used, such as the projective tests.

A major contribution of the psychologist to the field of psychiatry has been the production of tests and test procedures that give highly reliable results so that significant differences can be established between and among experimental and control groups. Such methodological advancements make possible a degree of quantification that would not otherwise exist and also make practical the use of relatively small groups of subjects and relatively short test intervals. Since interdisciplinary researches may involve preparations whose production is extremely time-consuming, the developments of the reliable test or test battery is a contribution of major importance.

Before and after the advent of psychologists, scientists (including psychiatrists) have devised behavioral tests which presumably measure a category defined by such frequently-used terms as drive, thinking, emotion, learning or motivation. Until relatively recently, little consideration was given to the scientific meaningfulness of these categories and the degree to which any or all tests measured these categories. The statistical demonstration of the reliability or unreliability within tests automatically led to measures of reliability between tests, that is, validity. Because the behavioral measure is the dependent variable for many interdisciplinary researches, the problem of test validity assumes paramount importance for this type of research. The large variety of behavior tests, the arrangement of tests into orderly batteries and the systematic scaling of many tests for difficulty, represent additional psychological achievement.

It is not uncommon, however, to find the impression that the psychologist is a person who merely gives tests, in effect, a psychometrician. To be sure, objective tests and measures are an important part of the psychologist's contribution to the diagnostic and prognostic picture, but his functions are no longer limited to an appraisal of intelligence or educational achievement. The total behavior and personality of an individual is assessed in the context in which he functions and the inner structure of personality is examined through the use of projective methods; and in some instances the laboratory procedures of the experimental or physiological psychologist are adapted to the study and investigation of the individual in the clinical setting.

In other words, the sensory and perceptual spheres are assessed for their intactness and normal range of function governing the acquisition of information.[62] The systems of action upon which performance and behavior depend are appraised. The central nervous system's integrative functions may be tested in a variety of ways ranging from the relatively simple and straightforward tests of perceptual function, memory, learning, attention, and so forth, to the more complex forms of association, conceptual thinking, serial or sequential perception and action. The processes by which the organism remains in equilibrium, both the internal regulatory mechanisms, and the adjustments made by the individual to the environment and his social interactions, may be studied under conditions unique and stressful.[59] New and old learning patterns may be observed under conditions of psychological conflict and physiological stress.

Psychological and psychiatric examination, including testing plus observation, requires the study of the individual in all life situations. It requires observation of the patient's reaction to the examiner, and also formal inquiry.[62] Because of the highly subjective nature of the material, histories will never be exacting and scientific, but insofar as they are orderly, logical and systematic, they are an invaluable aid. Systematization is necessary, not only for lucid understanding of the case in point, but for future reference and comparison by other clinicians. To date, though, psychologists have too often indulged in generalizations in their evaluations. What should be expected specifically in a psychological report is now considered briefly.

The data may well be broken into four basic elements: The primary information necessary includes the name, age, sex, marital status, special characteristics which are visible, and present location, also whether this report is written because it is part of an overall general examination for a psychiatrist, or whether it serves a specific function for a counselor.[34] This section should also include the conditions of the fact finding, whether the patient seemed relaxed, tense, nervous, rigid, or the like. The primary section of the holistic approach in psychological evaluation should also include attentiveness, facial expressions, posture and gait of walk.

The second area for investigation is the study of the perceptive qualities of the patient. A patient may fail to perceive accurately, or may perceive something that does not exist. His memory may be defective, or his ability to use his mind may be impaired, all of which may impede his perception. The appropriateness of his emotion, or perhaps even the total lack in this area, should be noted. By careful examination of how the patient perceives the outside world, how he reacts to and tests reality, how effective his reactions are towards the securing of his goals, the psychologist can obtain a picture of the level of functioning or dysfunctioning of the patient's perceptual system. A medical examination, in the case of dysfunction, should add to the knowledge of the causes for the dysfunction.

For the psychiatrist no less than for the psychologist, perception is called the primary step in reality testing, utilizing the response to environmental or reality stimulation. The ability to perceive includes functioning of the sensory organs, but an inability to perceive can mean dysfunction at any place along the line. To further test for reality contact and language facility, the subject is given an introspective report to discover what occupies the mind of the patient most of the time. In perception, the psychologist looks for alertness, accuracy, range, scope and reality assessment as normal characteristics. He could report dysfunction of perception attributes if the patient showed distractability, disorientation, confusion and illusion.

Cognative functions distinguish between the "normal or average" endowment, and the person's use of intellectualization under stressful situations. As normal characteristics, the psychologist seeks to report curiosity, memory, thoughts, talents and skills. He also looks for style of thought, creativity and logic. Manifestation of anamolies are found in meagerness, vagueness, worries, obsessions, inflexibility, and concreteness. The use of the autistic "I" in language is ofttimes symptomatic of an emotional disorder in need of therapy. Other language factors measure stereotypy, emotion and aggression.

Emotions are measured but must be noted in context rather than isolated, for emotional behavior is frequently merely an anxious response to a situation which seems threatening to the individual's well-being. In searching for emotionality, the examiner must look for depth and duration to gain an accurate assessment. Measurement in this area is highly subjective, but, again, the measurement is valid if taken in the context of the situation. The appropriateness of the emotion, or perhaps the lack of it should be noted. Energy level, effectiveness of action and persistence are normal reactions in emotion-laden situations, whereas stupor, rigidity, agitation and impulsiveness are signals of a disorder.

In reporting deviations of behavior, it is necessary for the examiner not only to note the context of the behavior (for this is paramount in the eventual nosology which will arise from a patterning of certain types of manifest behavior), but in addition to this the degree and frequency of occurrence must be noted in the psychological and psychiatric report, used in conjunction with basic interviews.

Supplementarily, the above are called part processes. The next areas to be considered by the examiner are the holistic processes, or the integrated functions of man. One attempts to discover self-conception and maturation, how he may relate to his wife or girlfriend or friends, how he feels about money or his car, and also how he relates to and feels about other people. In assessing these characteristics the psychologist, by means of projective techniques, tries to establish the patient's major attachments, and the relationship of these attachments, passive, dependent or independent. One also assesses sexual adjustment, and the transfer of early childhood experiences. The psychologist uncovers, in dealing with the Self, the individual's ego-identity, his level of aspiration, and his ethical and moral standards.

With these informational categories assessed, a team may then do a differential diagnosis on the individual patient. By checking reactive patterns, one might now distinguish between withdrawn, shy behavior and simple schizophrenia. Medical information will verify organicity and psychosomatic illness. Then the patient is ready to be treated. How he is to be treated depends upon the kind of illness and its severity. If, for example, the patient is a catatonic, then the psychiatrist, who may administer medication, will handle the case. However, in the case where there is a behavior problem, e.g., with a child, or perhaps a case of mild neurosis, both the psychologist and the psychiatrist may wish to treat with therapeutic methods.

IV

C ONTAINED within the statement of the Veterans Administration are words and concepts which are the subject
matter of considerable thought, discussion, and controversy.
Implied is the question: "Should psychologists practice psychotherapy?" This issue, more than any other, is seemingly
the bone of irritation, even contention, between psychiatry
and psychology; and it does in fact engender sharp, often
bitter, controversy.

Psychiatric opinion as officially put forth in a "Resolution
on Relations of Medicine and Psychology," approved by the
Board of Trustees of the American Medical Association, the
Council of the American Psychiatric Association, and the
Executive Council of the American Psychoanalytic Association, is as follows: "Psychiatry is the medical specialty concerned with illness that has chiefly mental symptoms. . . .
The systematic application of the methods of psychological
medicine to the treatment of illness, particularly as these
methods involve gaining an understanding of the emotional
state of the patient and aiding him to understand himself,
is called psychotherapy. This special form of medical treatment may be highly developed, but it remains simply one of
the possible methods of treatment to be selected for use according to medical criteria for use when indicated. Psychotherapy is a form of medical treatment and does not form
the basis for a separate profession."

A definitive reply to, or refutation of, the above is not
presumed to be within the purpose of this study. However,
certain points should be made. First, medicine historically

regards the human body as a physicochemical system; hence the title "physician," and the physical and pharmaceutical aspects of treatment which are basic in medicine. However, man is a social being too, and it is precisely this type of "treatment" that is administered by the psychologist, namely social, or communicative (talking and listening). Then, too, the concept of "normal" as dealt with earlier, is not the same to the psychiatrist as to the psychologist. To a physician, "normal" is a state in which there is an absence of pathology; while to a psychologist, "normal" is, among other things, a statistical concept, concerning the central distribution tendency of a group.

Psychiatrists and psychologists agree that, in institutional settings in which medical supervision and responsibility are established, there is often no practical problem or question as to who should "do psychotherapy." It would certainly seem that this matter should be transposed into questions concerning the qualifications, training, supervision, and safeguards for the patient, by all who undertake this form of treatment.

As indicated, probably the most controversial issue that provokes heated differences of opinion among psychologists and psychiatrists is the utilization of psychotherapy. We will not attempt to define the field at this point, and what it encompasses; but we do assume that in psychotherapy is included both short term and long term analysis, group psychotherapy, counselling in all its varieties, and every other form of therapy which does not make use of drugs.

The issue, then, is of course whether psychologists should be allowed to treat patients psychotherapeutically. We know that there is still strong opposition by the psychiatric profession to psychologists taking on patients for psychotherapy alone. The reasons for this opposition are many, but mainly center around the argument that psychologists without medical training might overlook or not recognize a problem which can be treated by a physician through use of drugs.

The psychologists may do a grave mistake, it is felt, by not sending a patient to a physician for a complaint which really is of physiological nature but mistaken for psychological in character. But the question is: Do not competent psychologists first refer a patient to a physician for a thorough examination for physical complaints, as stomach trouble, vomiting, or other symptoms, that might have their origin in the pathology of the body? Psychologists who are well-trained certainly do not assume that the basis of every complaint of a person lies with the psyche and not the soma.

But let us look also at the other side of the coin: The psychiatrist generally has most of his training in medical school and is more likely to look for the trouble in the soma; and most of his orientation may tend to disregard certain factors in the psychological field of his patient. The psychiatrist's psychology is oftentimes strongly influenced by biological thought. After all, psychiatry, neurology, and psychoanalysis do *not* have the answers to *all* problems; the attitude and approach of psychiatry to the field of psychotherapy might be too limited; and the refusal to let trained people from an allied profession utilize their approach effectively seems unwarranted on the ground indicated.

Therapeutic aspects have been touched on in Menninger's statement concerning the relationship between psychology and psychiatry. While most of the advances in psychotherapy probably have been made by psychiatrists starting with Charcot, Janet, Freud *et al.*, nevertheless some purely psychological advances have also been made. Psychologists such as Carl Rogers (with his client-centered approach and his research into psychotherapeutic evaluation), Rollo May, and others, have helped to further knowledge in this area. Group psychotherapy under men like Slavson has apparently been eagerly implemented by psychiatrists who have displayed great interest in group dynamics, therapy evaluation, and the importance of the non-professional persons such as attendants, occupational therapist, and others in the improvement of mental patients.[1]

The question of therapy brings up the matter of professional training. The training of psychiatrists is more specifically outlined than that of the psychologist. Psychologists are able to perform properly many activities in their field with training ranging from the A.B. degree through the Ph.D. degree plus internships. There are, to be sure, many functions of psychologists which do not involve counselling or therapy, and the psychologist who is involved in therapy must be one who is as fully prepared as possible. Therefore, in the discussion of treatment, the relationship of psychiatrist and psychologist is between those two practitioners who have the highest training in their respective fields.

The well-trained and accredited psychologist and psychiatrist may wish to use together general psychotherapy as their form of treatment. (Most psychoneurotic patients are treated this way.) The therapist, through mainly verbal (but oftentimes non-verbal) procedures, breaks through the repressed, troubling, symptom-producing conflicts of the patient; and, in time, the patient then understands his attitudes toward himself, his illness, and his environment.

A patient's difficulties may stem from both organic and emotional conditions, or either one alone. The chief purpose of diagnosis, then, is to determine what is possibly behind the disturbance, what kind of therapy may be most beneficial, and what outcome can be expected. The kind of therapy to be used depends upon the nature and severity of the patient's state and his personality make-up. (How does therapy work? There is no clear cut answer at this time. We should recogize that the field is open for new methods and techniques, experimental approaches of various kinds and well-grounded hypothesis for future advancement.) Psychologists as well as psychiatrists can work towards making significant strides in the art and science of psychotherapy.[60]

Kubie[33] has said: "The general medical attitude towards psychology tends to be uncomprehending; psychiatry is often grudging, reluctant, suspicious, excluding . . . It is wiser for medical schools and teaching hospitals to train clinical psychologists to be competent and skillful psychotherapists, offering them those elements of medical education which are essential for their scientific development, as well as for the protection of patients."

There is certainly much overlapping between psychology and psychiatry in the general area of mental hygiene.[50] For instance, the role of the psychologist is not only that of a tester, but also involves "real responsibility for case evaluation and therapeutic recommendation, or may involve therapeutic contacts and the supervision of training and research. There is no standardization. In one instance he may be a psychometrist, in another his duties may overlap greatly with a psychiatrist, in a third he may be strictly or mainly a scientist. There is no doubt, however, that since the Second World War large numbers of clinical psychologists are taking greater, often primary, responsibility for the diagnosis and treatment disposition of all kinds of clinical patients."[56]

Mental hygiene tries to bring to light in a person the unconscious, non-rational processes which cause phobias, temper tantrums, excess bullying, compulsions, and other troublesomeness, and equip him to recognize and reconstruct them. "Health," then, is the state of complete physical, mental, and social well-being, and not merely the absence of disease or infirmity.[58] "The mental health field encompasses three sets of objectives. One of these has to do with mentally sick people. For them the objective is the restoration of health. A second has to do with those people who are mentally healthy but who may become ill if they are not protected from conditions that are generally conducive to mental illness. The objectives for those persons is prevention. The third objective has to do with upbuilding of mental health of normal persons. This is positive mental health."[61] In this regard also, the psychiatrist and the psychologist are colleagues closely allied in a common endeavor.

In dealing with the role of the psychologist in psychotherapy with the crippled and disabled, Bychowski writes: "Conclusions derived from these data (psychological testing, assessment of specific cerebral functions, various projective
techniques) offer important cues for psychotherapy, a complex process in which the psychologist is called upon to play
his part."[10] Later, the role of the psychiatrist is discussed,
and it is pointed out that, on the basis of the psychiatric
examination, "and of all the other data, . . . a detailed program of psychological rehabilitation" is then established "in
which the various members of (our) team had their particular parts to play."[11]

As regards the various categories of mental cases, there are
at least three large categories for the psychiatrist and the
psychologist to collaborate on: (a) transient personality
disorders, (b) psychoneurotic, including the psychopathic
personality, and psychophysical disorders, and (c) psychoses.
It is only a layman's conception that the psychologist will be
concerned with the less seriously ill, the neurotics, and that
the psychologist will ordinarily not treat the seriously ill,
the psychotics. Actually, this separation is too rigid. The
psychiatrist treats many neurotics, and the psychologist does
have a part in the treatment of the psychotic together with
the psychiatrist.[65]

Psychotherapy is, after all, the application of psychological
techniques, facts, principles, and theories for the alleviation
of physical, mental, or psychosomatic disorder. "The objective of psychotherapy is to help disentangle the various self-
images an individual has, and to assist in bringing into
being a new self which is more nearly in tune with a newly
perceived reality."[3] For psychotherapy is a scientific tool and
an artful technique to help the individual understand his
emotional problems and their origins.

V

A large part of the problem of characterizing the relationships between psychiatrist and psychologist lies in the fact that it is only very recently, comparatively, that psychology has become a profession. The clinical and experimental aspects of the science have taken, fortunately or unfortunately, a leading part in this emergence. In so young a profession, there is naturally still a great deal of flux and of uncertainty as to where it stands; and, therefore, its relationships with other allied fields have not been clearly established.[64] It does not seem possible for these relationships to become clearly defined until the profession itself has acquired still more maturity.

Any lasting relationship between psychology and psychiatry that might evolve in the future will depend on the path that psychology as a profession follows in its growth. Psychodiagnosis and psychotherapy are distinctly matters of both art and science; in order for the art to be sound, the scientific aspect must continue to develop.[60] Is it possible for the psychologist to build his diagnostic tests and counselling procedures upon the theories of academic psychology? In the past, these two branches have developed rather independently of each other. The experimentalist has concerned himself with general laws of behavior in which segments or isolated functions have been viewed in their relationships to one another. There has been much less concern with the individual as he appears in the work of the psychologist or the psychiatrist. Today, however, there is a much greater tendency to use the individual as a unit of study, and this

48

will inevitably shorten the gap between general laws and personal behavior.

In this manner the art of psychodiagnosis and psychotherapy may be fortified with the necessary scientific basis. This path of development of psychology may well lead ultimately to a more clearly defined relationship with psychiatry; and psychiatry will be more closely related to all the branches of psychology if the individual is studied as a unit by the systematic psychologists.

Let us admit to a further view: All professionals realize that their education is not through or complete when formalized coursework has been completed. The professional attends seminars or conventions which help him to keep up with the ever increasing new knowledge that confronts his special field. It seems that it is just as important for him to become acquainted with the thinking in related fields especially because rapid growth in each field makes the possibility of further distance in thinking more evident.[7, 13, 17] This can be done by psychiatrists teaching psychologists *and* psychologists teaching psychiatrists. To harbor our knowledge and to keep it within ourselves can only lead to isolation, lack of communication, and additional misunderstanding. Journals from the different disciplines in a sense attempt to serve this capacity; but the amount which one has to read merely to keep up with his own field is so great that, except for an occasional article or two, it is almost impossible to read in other fields. Therefore, the answer may be in *interdiscipline teaching* to those in training rather than only to those already in the field.

Psychology offers to the field of psychiatry more than people with the same interests as psychiatrists.[57] Psychology has within its field those experimentalists, physiological psychologists, and educational and school psychologists whose efforts are related, if not directly aligned, to the field of psychiatry. Yet, these professionals have much to offer psychiatry in the everlasting plight for much needed information. To allow

ourselves in a related field to ignore or to lack the initiative
to learn from these allied fields is to do an injustice to our
own professions. It must be constantly remembered that all
of us, psychiatrist as well as psychologist, have obligations
toward one goal and that we must use each other's knowledge
for the future attainment of this goal. To insure our particular status quo is to be guilty of complacency. Complacency and progress do not coincide; and it is only in progress
that we may reach our ultimate in mental health standards.
Let no man or profession be omnipotent for with it we lead
ourselves to isolation and ultimately we perish professionally.

Our society is in continuing need of both kinds of practitioner, the psychiatrist and the psychologist. They are
needed separately, as well as together on the same team. For
the relationship between psychiatry and psychology is a dynamic one, and it must be therefore an inter-relationship, a
reciprocal intra-relationship in which each learns from and
teaches the other, a truly symbiotic relationship.

The psychiatrist, who adjusts people to society, and the
psychologist, who evaluates and collects data on behavior,
are of invaluable aid to each other. For the psychiatrist to
survive professionally without a knowledge of perception,
learning theory, or intelligence tests, would be difficult, and
similarly, for the psychologist to diagnose without the aid
of the field of medicine, would be foolhardy. Although their
training is different, and their goals and philosophies are
dichotomous in some areas, the functions of the psychiatrist
and the psychologist are necessarily complementary. In Menninger's[42] words, "Since the two disciplines are concerned
not with academic pursuits, but with the health and welfare
of people, our mutual obligation is to clarify misunderstanding and disagreement, to clarify interpersonal and working
relationships. Ignorance and criticism within each group concerning the other give rise to varying degrees of insecurity
and fears."

Tangentially, the number of psychologists is increasing so rapidly that this fact is itself of considerable note. A statistical survey shows that the American Psychological Association, of whom over 55 percent presently hold Ph.D. degrees, numbers more than 18,000, whereas the American Psychiatric Association has about 11,000 members. Additionally, psychologists feel that their education has given them certain rights, which rights have at times been misconstrued. It is the responsibility, therefore, of allied and parent groups to define these rights for the good of all. The psychologist sometimes feels that perhaps the greater the distance between him and the psychiatrist, the greater his feeling of security. Here lies another pitfall. The American Psychological Association, representing the psychologists, should not be forced to seek distance from the American Psychiatric Association for security, but should seek proximity for security. Further, coercion has proved unwise on the part of psychiatry in dealing with psychology. Coercion only threatens freedom in this vital field.

The question of the right of psychiatry to dominate psychology is irrelevant. It is a question of policy only, which resolves itself to whether it is not to the interest of psychiatry to make the psychologists more effective professionally. The only way to restore tranquility is to admit psychologists into the full field of mental hygiene; and give to them the feeling that it is in the best interests of the whole, since a house divided cannot stand. Psychiatrists and psychologists should be able to work together for a common purpose.[63] Each member of the team has a particular contribution to make; but, in making it, must do so in cooperation with the other members. This cooperative approach to be successful, however, must possess, among other values or characteristics, the recognition on the part of each participant of his own limitations as well as his possible contributions and, at the same time, a real respect for what each has to offer. This kind of intimate working together for a common purpose, in this instance, the total health and welfare of the individual, is a relatively new and, frequently, very threatening experience to many professional workers, but it holds great hope ultimately for helping to bring about what is so badly needed today—a happy and beneficial relationship between psychiatry and psychology. Emphasis on such areas of friendly competition and exchange of knowledge must be increased, if there is to be peaceful coexistence based on mutual respect.

Psychology and psychiatry, both in cooperation with each other and independently, are certainly making great strides in the imperative task of improving mental health. This is the goal toward which their improved relationship must carry them, regardless of any other considerations. Any relationship that develops on this basis will prove sound and mutually satisfying.

There are at least four specific types of contribution that the psychologist can make to the attempt on the part of the psychiatrist to aid and benefit the patient. These are diagnosis, research, administration, and training. As regards diagnosis, the classical and traditional contribution of the psychologist to the psychiatrist has been the quantitative evaluations of certain mental functions that he has been able to make through the use of tests and measures. The psychologist and the psychiatrist are today concerned with one thing in common: The exposure and definition of areas of disability in function with a view to affecting the patient's selection of other and non-disabling responses.

The second and classically traditional contribution of the psychologist has been in the field of research. His extensive and intensive training in the research techniques applicable to studies of human behavior and his knowledge regarding experimental design equips the psychologist very well. While this affects patients indirectly, there is a more direct effect on the psychiatrist. There is a beneficial effect on the psychiatrist of an ever-present research attitude which the psychologist is able to demonstrate in his approach to an evaluation of case material. The presence of the research attitude in the person of the psychologist tends to emphasize day after day that the last words have by no means been said or written regarding human behavior, and thus urge the psychiatrist to express his own curiosity in whatever form of clinical research his past training allows him. The psychologist's formal training in anthropology, sociology, experimental, social and educational psychology entailing as this does a broad and intensive survey of the literature both past and present, makes him uniquely fitted to appreciate both the relationships of isolated findings and impressions with the main body of knowledge already amassed concerning them.

A third contribution concerns administrative duties in the clinic, hospital or office itself where the psychiatrist and psychologist work together. Because of the need for making records of maximum use and indeed even accessible for research purposes, the psychologist may well assume for the psychiatrist the responsibility for what could be adjudged adequate clinical record-keeping, case-closing, coding of cases, and follow-up.

Also, on the quasi-administrative side there are certain inter-agency relationships that can be initiated and evaluated by the psychologist rather than by the psychiatrist. We refer now to relationships with the school systems. The psychologist most immersed in the data relative to human abilities and aptitudes, and the vagaries therein, is the one most conversant with the technical problems of handling them and best appreciates the results of their appearance in the classroom. Relationships and evaluation of schools, special classes, public or private remedial units are duties that may adequately be carried out for the psychiatrist by the psychologist.

As regards training, in the non-organized teaching content that the psychologist gives to those in psychiatry, much through propinquity or perhaps osmosis can be learned.

In a more formal way the psychologist can be of great worth in formal seminars and group discussions. The psychologist can also be of great help in formal instruction to students of related disciplines in scientific methods of investigation. Both psychiatrists and psychologists can and should assist others in study, but the latter is usually more familiar with an adequate handling of specific problems of research design, the relative merits and applicability of various research methods, and approaches in considering various types of investigations.

Essentially, then, it is entirely possible and extremely necessary today that there be a coordination of the efforts of all the experts, notably the psychiatrist and psychologist, to work harmoniously together supplementing each other in their various areas of specialization so that the *whole* patient, the *total personality,* will receive the maximum benefits from the two sources that will redound to the welfare ultimately of our society. Discussing psychology's contribution to medicine, Menninger again states that "it brings to medicine also a tradition of objective measurement, of clearly defined logic, of proper methodological procedure which clinical practice and clinical thinking tend to make us forget and neglect. Traditional psychiatric nosology has finally been forced into open bankruptcy, largely by the penetrating symptomotological analyses made by the psychologists. And a healthy state of affairs it is, I say. We can now begin to define with a precision long absent from our work the clinical factors—psychological and otherwise—which characterize similar syndromes." Menninger feels, summarily, that the psychologist's therapeutic function will eventually find its place "in the same way that the therapeutic function of the X-rays has found its place . . ."[19]

VI

Today the fields of psychiatry and psychology are vast and undermanned. In all probability the need will continue to increase with the growing interest in mental health, since general insecurity and anxiety seem to characterize our times. Psychology as a professional activity began with the study of behavior problems and maladjustments. Psychiatry as a professional activity began chiefly with psychotic patients and worked down or up, as the case may be, to neuroses, behavior disorders, character disturbances, psychosomatic conditions and, in a minor way, to international relations. So psychology and psychiatry tend to fuse and diffuse.

In hospitals, schools and clinics for the mentally retarded, together the psychologist and the psychiatrist contribute much to the help, education and growth of the mentally retarded child. Proper diagnosis, psychologically and physiologically determined through physical and psychological examinations, can determine the proper treatment for a given child. Only together can the best help be given. For example, if a child is considered to be mentally retarded, and then psychological examination reveals that there are possible organic factors, this can be investigated more fully by the psychiatrist and the neurologist. Certainly medical examination is needed. The psychologist cannot make the appropriate diagnosis without this information. Nor can the pediatrician make the diagnosis fully of mental retardation when in fact the child may have severe or definite emotional reasons for not responding.

55

Currently, both psychologists and psychiatrists should be concerned with working out a more adequate interdisciplinary approach; each can learn from the other. The psychologists can teach research and test design in the medical schools, and the psychiatrists can set up programs for the training of psychologists in clinical methods with particular emphasis on somatic aspects of mental disturbance. There should be no dychotomy in the understanding of mind and body. It might be possible in time to set up a program under which psychotherapists could earn a degree of, say, "Doctor of Psychological Medicine" or "Doctor of Psychological Services."

In a culture which is as competitive as ours, it is necessary for practitioners in psychiatry and psychology to have sufficient maturity and insight, in the interests of the patient, the community and scientific progress. Interprofessional adjustment problems have to be worked out so that the psychiatrist and psychologist can work together cooperatively. For the psychiatrist and the psychologist both play an important role in the diagnosis, treatment *and* prevention of mental illness. Neither one should be underestimated, nor overestimated.

The solution of our major social problems can be arrived at through the combined efforts of experts in many areas of human understanding. Psychiatry, psychology, sociology and anthropology are all devoted to the study of how men act and feel. Psychiatry has accumulated an extensive body of knowledge about the anatomy and the physiology of personality. It has seemingly arrived at an explanation, at least in theory, of the possible causes of man's aggression toward, and regression from, his environment, and self. It has contributed mainly to the understanding of the effect of the environment on the individual, his phylogeny, the needs of the individual created by the pressing situation which surrounds him, and how his personality is an expression of his needs, and may reflect his inner states of tension and drive.

Comprehension resulting from all points of view and insight gained from a combination of disciplines, including psychiatric, psychologic, and social work, is Shakow's[58] view-point in these words: "Instead of dichotomy in thinking and method, there should be a team approach that offers the patient a type of service that will be contiguous, collateral, ancillary, articulative and integrative. The essence of true team activity is coordinated thinking of persons with different points of view growing out of different training. Controversy is based on old complexes of terms: supervision, direction, and guidance versus collaboration, association, and co-operation."

SUMMARY

THE relationships, inter-relationships, and intra-relationships of psychiatry and psychology are rather definite and substantiable. The psychiatrist in his medical evaluation determines the organ pathology associated with mental disease. It is a highly specialized procedure including metabolic functions, cardiac functions, blood and spinal fluid tests for syphilis, and other CNS syndrome, and reflex or other tests for brain tumors and other pathology of the nervous system, including, too, the use of the electroencephalograph. Medical therapy for the mentally ill includes psychotherapy, shock treatment, narcosis therapy, electronarcosis, psychosurgery, physiotherapy, biochemotherapy.[13]

The psychologist, through the psychological evaluation of the patient, based upon observation, interviews with the patient, psychological test batteries to determine intelligence, personality, organization and capacities, aids in the diagnosis and treatment of the patient.

The findings of the both disciplines together have much to offer each other. As our scientific knowledge grows, we may be able to establish conditions for better physical and psychological welfare in which each individual may develop to his fullest potential and utilize his resources for the betterment of society.

Conflict and competition between the two professions have been seen in the past and still exist today although with diminishing intensity. Much of the conflict and competition which plague the professions came about, as indicated earlier, through mere immaturity. (By immaturity is meant not immaturity of individuals on an emotional, social or intellectual level but rather the relatively short lifespan that these two professions have lived with each other.) With the lack of time, set orientations of true purpose were nil and the sharing of associated interests without precise disciplines led to some suspicions and mistrusts. (It is well recognized that we are more initiated by the blemishes of our closest relatives than we are by the derelictions of strangers. Psychologists and psychiatrists have given evidence of a family feud.) But these differences offer a potential of collaboration and compatibility. Within this conflict will come the necessary growth for more productive and fruitful teamwork. Inherent in the team approach is the postulate that teamwork recognizes that professions, as well as nations, cannot realize their full development in isolation. Isolation can only lead to more suspicion, threat, and misunderstanding.

Cooperative teamwork is essential to better understanding especially within the two disciplines of psychiatry and psychology. Further need for teamwork is compelled by the vast complexity of the human being; it is now recognized that people are (1) biological, (2) social, (3) cultural, and (4) interpersonal entities. In itself, this view does not lend itself to the total impact that it truly implies. When one thinks of all the variables which make up these four broad categories, it is subsequently and rightfully concluded that an unbelievably extensive amount of knowledge is needed in order to understand the complexity of an individual as a whole. The extent of this knowledge is so engulfing that to expect any one individual to be proficient in this understanding is to ask too much. Hence, specialized training is necessary.

Therefore we, as in any other field which is intricate in nature and overwhelmed with specialties, must rely and depend upon others in order to draw out all the information which is pertinent to our work. We now see the need for teamwork. *Professional teamwork,* by definition, is a cooperative approach which serves to bring forth understanding among the different disciplines within the team and helps each to clarify his efforts to the other members of the team via a personalized contact.

It seems obvious that what is most needed presently is more research in both psychiatry and psychology. But the research must be in collaboration; it must bring together psychologists and psychiatrists to work on problems of common interest. Thus, for instance, the psychologist should carry on research but not in a vacuum; he must tie in his findings and his designs with the total field both of psychology and of clinical psychiatry. In part, psychiatry is based on psychological principles, and these must be examined and reinvestigated again and again in light of new findings.

Research in the special areas of diagnosis and therapy is perhaps most needed. Our tools are still too imperfect to win true scientific status. There is a need for more investigation of projective techniques. But psychology may contribute most, in our time, to psychiatry in the field of therapy if it could devise tools similar to the diagnostic ones. Which patients are most likely to succeed in therapy? What kind of therapy and treatment are best for what kinds of problem?

Still another way of improving the professional relationships between the two disciplines is closer contact between the men and women working in the fields. This is said not only in terms of institutions, clinics, and hospitals, but also in relation to private practice. There just is not enough communication between psychologists and psychiatrists. More reciprocal professional meetings might be additionally effective in the betterment of relationships. Genuine acceptance on the part of both disciplines of the individual as the most important entity may serve to smooth out details which presently concern overmuch both psychologists and psychiatrists.

REFERENCES

1. Albee, George W.: *Mental Health Manpower Trends*. New York, Basic Books, Inc., 1959.
2. Allen, Frederick H.: Psychiatry: Progress in Orthopsychiatry, *American Journal of Orthopsychiatry*, Vol. *25*, No. 3, July 1955, pp. 479-490.
3. Anderson, Camilla M.: *Saints, Sinners and Psychiatry*. Philadelphia, J. B. Lippincott Company, 1950, p. 135.
4. Andrews, T. G., Editor: *Methods of Psychology*. New York, John Wiley and Sons, Inc., 1948, Chapter 19.
5. Arieti, Silvano, M.D., Editor: *American Handbook of Psychiatry*. New York, Basic Books, Inc., 1960. Prefatory statement.
6. Beck, Samuel J. and Molish, Herman B., Editor: *Reflexes to Intelligence*. Glencoe, Illinois, The Free Press, 1958.
7. Blain, Daniel: The Psychiatrist and the Psychologist, *Journal of Clinical Psychology*, Vol. *3*, 1947, pp. 4-10.
8. Burton, A. and Harris, R.: *Clinical Studies of Personality*. New York, Harper and Bros., 1955.
9. Brussel, James A.: *Layman's Guide to Psychiatry*. New York, Barnes and Noble, Inc., 1961.
10. Bychowski, Gustav: Psychotherapy with the Crippled and Disabled, in *Specialized Techniques in Psychotherapy*, edited by G. Bychowski, and J. L. Despert, New York, Basic Books, Inc., 1952, p. 187.
11. Bychowski: *Ibid.,* p. 189.
12. Cameron, Norman A. and Margaret, Ann: *Behavior Pathology*. Boston, Houghton, Mifflin Co., 1951.
13. Coleman, J.: *Abnormal Psychology and Modern Life*. New York, Scott, Foresman Co., 1956.
14. Drever, James: *A Dictionary of Psychology*. Harmondsworth,

Middlessex, Penguin Books, Ltd., 1958, p. 227.

15. Dunbar, Flanders: *Synopsis of Psychosomatic Diagnosis and Treatment*. St. Louis, C. V. Mosby Company, 1948.

16. Frosch, J. and Ross, N.: *The Annual Survey of Psychoanalysis*, Vol. V. New York, International Universities Press, 1954.

17. Graduate Internship Training in Psychology: *Journal of Consulting Psychology*, Vol. 9, 1945, pp. 243-266.

18. *Ibid.*, p. 1.

19. Hall, Bernard H., Editor: *A Psychiatrist's World: Selected Papers of Karl Menninger*. New York, The Viking Press, 1959, pp. 395-415, 690-696.

20. Havemann, E.: *The Age of Psychology*. New York, Simon and Schuster, Inc., 1957.

21. Hinsie, Leland E., and Shatzky, Jacob: *Psychiatric Dictionary*. New York, Oxford University Press, 1947, p. 438.

22. Hinsie and Shatzky: *Ibid.*, p. 437.

23. Hinsie and Shatzky: *Op. Cit.*, p. 443.

24. Hoch, P. and Zubin, J.: *Relation of Psychological Tests to Psychiatry*. New York, Grune and Stratton, 1952.

25. Hodges, A. and Hawkinson, J.: Contributions of Psychology to Psychiatry, *American Journal of Psychiatry*, Vol. *112*, No. 9, March 1956.

26. Hutchings, Richard H.: *A Psychiatric Word Book: A Lexicon of Terms*, 7th Edition. Utica, The State Hospitals Press, 1943, p. 201.

27. Hutchings: *Ibid.*, p. 197.

28. Joint Report on Relations Between Psychology and Psychiatry: *The American Psychologist*, Vol. *15*, March 1960, p. 198.

29. Jones, Ernest: *Life and Work of Sigmund Freud*. New York, Basic Books, Inc., 1957, pp. 287-301.

30. Kanner, Leo: *Child Psychiatry*. Springfield, Thomas, Publishers, 1948, p. 7.

31. Kanner: *Ibid.*, pp. 99-103.

32. Krout, Maurice H., Editor: *Psychology, Psychiatry and the Public Interest*. Minneapolis, University of Minnesota Press, 1956.

33. Kubie, Lawrence S.: Medical Responsibility for Training in Clinical Psychology, *Journal of Clinical Psychology*, Vol. *V.*, 1949, pp. 1-94.
34. Law, Stanley G.: *Therapy Through Interview.* New York, McGraw-Hill Company, 1948.
35. Levy, D. M.: Present State of Child Psychiatry, *American Journal of Psychiatry*, Vol. *108*, 1952, pp. 481-488.
36. Lewis, N. D. C.: General Considerations in Therapeutic Failures, in *Failures in Psychiatric Treatment*, edited by P. H. Hoch. New York, Grune and Stratton, 1948, p. 1.
37. Luborsky, Holt: *Personality Patterns of Psychiatrists.* New York, Basic Books, Inc., 1958.
38. Luszki, Margaret B.: *Interdisciplinary Team Research.* New York University Press, 1958. pp. 76-77.
39. Masserman, Jules H.: *Principles of Dynamic Psychiatry.* Philadelphia: W. B. Saunders Co., 1946, p. 3.
40. Masserman: *Ibid.,* p. 293.
41. May, Rollo, Angel, Ernest, and Ellenberger, Henri F., Editors: *Existence: A New Dimension in Psychiatry and Psychology.* New York, Basic Books, Inc., 1958.
42. Menninger, K. A.: The Relationships of Clinical Psychology and Psychiatry, *The American Psychologist,* Vol. *5*, No. 3, 1950.
43. Menninger, William C.: *Psychiatry.* Ithaca, Cornell University Press, 1948.
44. Modlin, H. C. and Faris, M.: Follow-up Study of Psychiatric Team Functioning, *Bulletin* of the Menninger Clinic, 18, 242, 1954.
45. Morgan, James: Training Clinical Psychologists in the Veterans Administration, *Journal of Clinical Psychology,* Vol. *3*, 1957, pp. 28-33.
46. Munn, Norman L.: *Psychology.* Boston, Houghton-Mifflin Co., 1956.
47. Newsletter: *The New York State Psychologist,* Special Issue, The New York State Psychological Association, November, 1960.
48. Pearson, G.: *Emotional Disorders of Children.* New York, W. W. Norton, 1949.

49. Pearson, G.: *Psychoanalysis and the Education of the Child.* New York, W. W. Norton and Co., 1954.
50. Prados, M.: On Mental Health, *Journal of Canadian Medical Association,* Vol. *74,* April 15, 1956.
51. Raimy, Victor C.: *Progress in Clinical Psychology,* Volume I, Section 2 on Professional Issues. New York, Grune and Stratton, 1952.
52. Redlich, Frederick C. and Hollingshead, August B.: *Social Class and Mental Illness.* New York, Wiley and Sons, 1958.
53. Rosenzweig, Saul: *Psychodiagnosis.* New York, Grune and Stratton, 1949.
54. Rosenzweig: *Ibid.,* p. 1.
55. Schafer, R.: *The Clinical Application of Psychological Tests.* New York, International Universities Press, 1948.
56. Shaffer, G. Wilson: *Fundamental Concepts in Clinical Psychology.* New York, McGraw-Hill Book Co., 1952, p. 25.
57. Shaffer, L. F.: Clinical Psychology and Psychiatry, *Journal of Consulting Psychology,* 11, 5, 1947.
58. Shakow, David: Psychology and Psychiatry: A Dialogue, *American Journal of Orthopsychiatry,* Part I, Vol. *19,* 1949, p. 191-200; Part II, Vol. *19,* 1949, p. 381ff.
59. Silverman, Hirsch Lazaar: The Psychology and Psychiatry of Harry Stack Sullivan, *The Psychiatric Quarterly Supplement.* Vol. *29,* Part I, 1955, pp. 7-22.
60. Silverman, Hirsch Lazaar: Psychotherapy: A Survey and Evaluation. *The Psychiatric Quarterly Supplement,* Vol. 36, Part I, 1962, pp. 116-135.
61. Stevenson, George S.: *Mental Health Planning for Social Action.* New York, McGraw-Hill Book Co., 1956, p. 207.
62. Sullivan, H. S.: *The Psychiatric Interview.* New York, W. W. Norton and Co., 1953.
63. Tolman, R. S.: Psychiatry and The Public Interest: Book Review, *Journal of Projective Techniques,* 21, 98, 1957.
64. Watson, Robert I.: *Psychology as a Profession.* New York, Doubleday, Doran and Co., 1954.
65. Young, Robert A.: The Status of the Clinical Psychologist in Therapy, *American Journal of Orthopsychiatry,* Vol. 20, 1950, pp. 311-314.

INDEX